Four Pals™
at the Park

(An Adventure with Friends who are Different)

By Angel Tucker
and
Robert A. Rohm, Ph.D.

Illustrated by Steve Pileggi

Personality
INSIGHTS
PRESS

Four Pals™ at the Park

By
Angel Tucker
and
Robert A. Rohm, Ph.D.

Illustrations by Steve Pileggi
Editors, Nancy Marbry and Shirley Voorhees
Graphic design by Pedro A. Gonzalez

Published by

Personality
INSIGHTS
PRESS

Printed in the United States of America

ISBN: 978-0-9841121-1-1

ACKNOWLEDGMENTS
for "Four Pals"™ Series 1

First, I'd like to thank God, who is the creator of ALL things – including our personalities! Psalms 139:14 says that we are all "fearfully and wonderfully made" and "marvelous are thy works!" I'm so thankful that He made us all different! Just think how crazy the world would be if we were all the same!

Next, I'd like to thank my husband, Dennis, for being so supportive of the development of these books and encouraging me when I thought they would never get finished! Also, to my four children, who have kept me from ever having a dull moment! I love and appreciate each of them!

I want to thank Madison for her input and excitement about the books from an 11 year olds' point of view. She is a blessing!

A huge thank you to Steve Pileggi, illustrator of this series, for his creativity and ability to make the stories come alive! Much was asked of him, in a very short period of time, and he came through with flying colors! He is truly amazing!

Last, but certainly not least, words cannot even begin to express my thanks to the Personality Insights Team for seeing my vision for these books and committing to countless hours of hard work and editing to make the "Four Pals" series a reality. Many children will benefit from their selfless efforts! A special thanks to Dr. Robert Rohm, Nancy Marbry, Shirley Voorhees, and Pedro Gonzalez. Their individual talents have been invaluable in this project! God Bless them!

Angel Tucker
C.H.B.C
National Christian Speaker
Author
Proverbs 3:5-6

When writing a children's book series such as this, you face several challenges: First, you want each book to be simple and easy to understand. Second, you do not want any child to feel labeled or "put down," rather you want them to feel encouraged and "lifted up." (The entire D-I-S-C Model of Human Behavior is not about what is wrong with you – it is a wellness model – it is about what is right with you!) Third, you want each child to gain understanding of how to grow to be a well-balanced person using the traits from all four personality styles. In a word, you hope the books are educational.

I believe, with the help and efforts of the dedicated team of people who put these books together (Angel Tucker, Nancy Marbry, Shirley Voorhees, Pedro Gonzalez, Steve Pileggi, and myself) that we have achieved all of the above goals. I hope you will agree!

Robert A. Rohm, Ph.D.
Personality Insights, Inc.
Atlanta, GA
www.personalityinsights.com
1-800-509-DISC (3472)

Welcome to the "Four Pals"™ Series!

These books were created for three reasons:

1. To show children that God is the creator of everything – even our personalities!

2. To teach children all about the different personality types!

3. To let children know that it's okay to feel unique and special as well as be different from their friends!

Here is a further description of each of the personality types. This should assist you in giving your children a better idea of how God made each of us different. The important fact to remember is that all children have a unique blend of ALL FOUR of these personality styles. No one will fit neatly into one style. All children will possess some of all of these traits and will exhibit each of the four different types of behavior at different times. Usually, however, one style will emerge as the most predominant trait and this will be the trait the child will demonstrate most often. It will also be the trait that he or she will be most comfortable using on a daily basis. We often say, "That is the way they are wired!"

David

DAVID is our wonderful "D" type personality! The letter "D" represents the word "**Dominant.**" "D" type personalities love to be in charge and have things done their way. "D"s think fast and move fast! Their communication style is bottom line. Their attitude is lead, follow, or get out of my way! You never have to wonder what a "D" is thinking – they will just tell you! "D" children are usually the ones leading all the group activities and telling all the other kids what they will be doing. God bless the **Outgoing/Task-Oriented** "D" type personality!

For more great tips on understanding the D-I-S-C child, please get a copy of *A+ Ideas for Every Student's Success* at www.personalityinsights.com or www.personalityprofiles.org

Iris

IRIS is our wonderful "I" type personality! The letter "I" represents the word "**Inspiring**." "I" type personalities love to have fun! They are very optimistic and outgoing! They tend to be forgetful at times because they are usually in a hurry to do things! They also move fast! Their communication style is exciting and enthusiastic. They don't do well with lots of details and information and may have difficulty accomplishing tasks because they lose their focus. They love being around other people, thrive on attention and love to entertain others! God bless the **Outgoing/People-Oriented** "I" type personality!

Summer

SUMMER is our wonderful "S" type personality! The letter "S" represents the word "**Supportive**." "S" type personalities are very compliant and pleasant. They do not like conflict. They like peace and harmony. They sometimes have trouble making decisions because they tend to make up their minds slowly. Their communication style is "easy-going." In other words, they tend to adapt easily to whatever is going on around them in their environment. They love people and relationships! "S"s love being around other people and helping everyone they meet. They are sensitive and sometimes get their feelings hurt easily. They like to feel appreciated and secure. God bless the **Reserved/People-Oriented** "S" type personality!

Charlie

CHARLIE is our wonderful "C" type personality! The letter "C" represents the word "**Cautious**." "C" type personalities enjoy having a routine and schedule. They are usually very good students and like things that challenge their mind. Their communication style is A to Z, which means that, details and planning are very important to a "C." That is why they ask so many questions. The "C" type personality prefers to do things that have been planned out especially if it involves a large group of people. They are very comfortable being alone and working independently. They appreciate quality more than quantity. God bless the **Reserved/Task-Oriented** "C" type personality!

The "**Four Pals**" series is designed to have 1 book in each series that highlights each of the four different personality styles. There will be 4 more books released in the future.
www.personalityinsights.com/fourpals or www.personalityprofiles.org

One sunny Saturday, a little boy named David thought it would be an awesome day to go to the park.

David did not want to go to the park alone, so he quickly decided to call some of his friends and tell them to go with him. David loved to be in charge and was sure he could get his friends to go to the park.

The first person he called was his friend Iris. Iris loved to have fun! She squealed with delight when David told her that he wanted her to go to the park. She jumped up and down and said, "This is going to be so exciting!"

"Okay," said David. "Meet me by the big slide at 10 o'clock."

"I'll be there!" Iris replied happily.

Next, David phoned his friend, Summer. He said, "Iris and I are going to the park. Meet us at the big slide at 10 o'clock."

Summer felt so special because they invited her to go to the park also. She loved being with her friends.

Summer noticed that it was 9:00 o'clock and if she hurried, she could bake some cookies for them to eat at the park. Summer loved doing things for others.

Finally, David called his friend, Charlie. He told Charlie that Iris, Summer and he were going to the park and that he should join them. Charlie hesitated and said, "I didn't plan to go to the park today. I usually organize my room and my closet and my toys on Saturdays."

12

David grunted and said, "Do that later! We're meeting at 10 o'clock by the big slide." Charlie reluctantly agreed and was flustered because he now had to hurry and organize his room.

Before David knew it, it was close to 10 o'clock
and he headed to the big slide.

When he arrived at the slide, Summer was already there. She looked relieved when she saw David.

"I'm so glad you're here! I wasn't sure if I was at the right slide. I baked us some cookies! Thanks so much for inviting me!"

Charlie then arrived precisely at 10 o'clock. He had sunscreen for each of them to put on.

David said, "Where's Iris?" Summer was worried that maybe she was lost. Charlie was upset that she wasn't there exactly at 10 o'clock!

17

About fifteen minutes later, Iris finally arrived. She had
a big smile on her face and her hair was in pony tails!
"Isn't my hair cute?" she asked. "Guess what! I have a
big surprise!"

Not even listening to Iris about her surprise, David scolded, "Where were you? We've been waiting for fifteen minutes!"

"I'm sorry," Iris replied. "I lost track of time." Iris was always losing track of time.

"Well, let's stop wasting time now," exclaimed David.
"Let's go play on the monkey bars." David ran at full speed.
He was determined to be the first one there.

Iris did cartwheels all the way to the monkey bars.
"That was fun!" she said.

Summer walked carefully so she wouldn't fall and drop the cookies.

Charlie walked down the sidewalk so he wouldn't get dirt in his shoes. He decided to watch the others on the monkey bars for a little while. He did not want to get blisters on his hands.

After they were finished playing on the monkey bars, Iris said, "That merry-go-round looks fun! Let's go there next!" David said, "I want to go to the swings and then to the slide."

David then told everyone to follow him. He ran quickly towards the swings shouting, "Me first!"

After they finished playing, Summer asked, "Would anyone like some cookies?" "Yeah!" said David, "I want the biggest one."

Iris was having great fun with her cookie! She was breaking it into pieces and popping them into her mouth!

Charlie said, "I am going to wash my hands before I eat my cookie," and he headed off to the restroom.

Summer made sure everyone else had enough cookies before she ate any.

After they finished their cookies, David said, "It's time to go. I need to get home now."

"Thanks again for inviting me," said Summer. "I had a wonderful time."

"Me too!" Iris said. "Friends are fun!"

Then Charlie said, "Iris, I believe there was something you wanted to tell us earlier. What was it?"

"Oh yeah," said Iris. "I almost forgot! My mom said she would take us to the zoo next Saturday. Can all of you come?"

Each of her friends said they would be able to come as long as their mom or dad said it was okay. This made Iris incredibly happy and she jumped up and down. Iris loved the idea of everyone going to the zoo together! Iris said, "Awesome! When I say my prayers tonight, I will have something else to be thankful for!"

"Yeah, me too!" each of her friends replied. And they all went home glad that even though they were all very different, they could still be great friends and have great adventures together.

Reader's Guide

This is Book 1 in this series. The focus in this book is on David – the **Dominant** "D" type personality! To get all four books in the "Four Pals" series go to the website: www.personalityinsightsights.com/fourpals or call 1-800-509-DISC (3472)

David

Did you notice in this story how David likes to be in charge? He doesn't seem to consider the fact that at times, he might be coming across a little "bossy" to his friends. He is a natural born "take charge" kind of person. This personality style is often looked at as a natural born leader. If he uses this trait in the right way, he will grow up to become an outstanding leader who will influence many, many people.

Iris

Did you observe in this story how Iris likes to have fun and play? She occasionally does not pay close enough attention to detail and appears to be "unfocused" at times. But, everyone loves her because of her happy nature! She is a natural born talker and a very energetic kind of person. She is always helping everyone around her to have fun. If she uses this trait in the right way she will always help other people to feel happy and laugh a lot!

Charlie

Did you notice in this story how Charlie liked to have everything in order in his life? Charlie believes it is important to obey the rules and to do things right! Sometimes Charlie is very serious, but he is working on having a little more fun. He is an excellent student and does well in school. Charlie may enjoy becoming a physician, a pilot, an accountant, a lawyer, or a scientist. If he uses his traits in the right way, he will grow up to be very successful in whatever area he studies!

Summer

Did it warm your heart to watch the way Summer helped all of her friends? She was thoughtful and cared about what other people might want. She consistently put her friends ahead of herself, which is a good thing to do. She is also learning that she is important and has needs, too! If she uses her traits in the right way, she will make a lot of people feel special. When you hear someone say, "Have a nice day," they are really saying, "I hope you meet a lot of people like Summer" or "I hope you act like Summer today and are kind and gentle towards everyone you meet!"

About the Authors

Angel Tucker is a wife, mom and national speaker/trainer. As a Certified Human Behavior Consultant and owner of Personality Profiles, LLC, she has been speaking and training professionally across North America for the past 18 years. She began by teaching churches and youth groups. She instantly knew it was her desire to share this life changing information with as many people as possible. Angel and her husband Dennis, who is an officer in the United States Air Force, have four children – Danielle, Chase, Hannah and Elijah. When Dennis retires, they plan to travel the country together – teaching and training others about our wonderful God-given personalities!

If you are interested in having Angel speak at your next engagement, please contact her using the following information:

Website: www.personalityprofiles.org
Email: personalitypro@msn.com

Dr. Robert A. Rohm is a renowned National and International speaker. He has traveled all over the world including every continent (except Antarctica), teaching and training people in the D-I-S-C Model of Human Behavior. Most people consider Dr. Rohm to be one of the leading authorities in the world on understanding personality styles and relationship dynamics.

Dr. Rohm has been an educator for over 40 years. He has earned 5 college degrees and has written or co-authored over 20 books and over 350 published articles. He also has numerous audio and video training programs.

Dr. Rohm is a father and grandfather and believes that has been the true source for many of his insights and learning experiences. He has entertained and enlightened audiences for many years. His mixture of stories, illustrations, and humor make him a gifted speaker to audiences of all ages!

Dr. Rohm is also the co-founder of discoveryreport.com

To learn more about Dr. Robert Rohm or have him at your event, go to: www.robertrohm.com or www.personalityinsights.com or call Personality Insights, Inc. at (800) 509-DISC (3472)

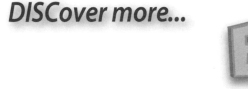

The "Four Pals" series is designed to have 1 book in each series that highlights one of the personality styles. There will be 4 more books released in the future. To find out more go to:

www.personalityinsights.com/fourpals

or

www.personalityprofiles.org

Watch for our next "Four Pals" Series 2:
Four Pals at the Pool
Four Pals at the Circus
Four Pals in a Parade
Four Pals on a Field Trip

OUTGOING & TASK

OUTGOING & PEOPLE

RESERVED & TASK

RESERVED & PEOPLE

D I C S

For more in-depth understanding of personality styles visit us:

For an autographed copy visit
Angel Tucker at:
www.personalityprofiles.org

www.personalityinsights.com
or contact us at:
Personality Insights inc.
P.O. BOX 28592 Atlanta, GA 30358-0592
800.509.DISC (3472)
info@personalityinsights.com

Personality
INSIGHTS
PRESS